Ribblehead Re-born

Ribblehead Re-born

by
W R Mitchell

Visuals: Peter Fox
With the advice and support
of
A P Freschini (Resident Engineer)
and
Geoff Bounds (Project Manager, Settle-Carlisle)

Castleberg
1992

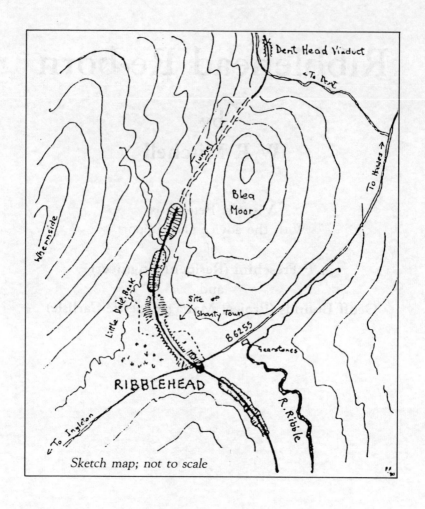

Sketch map; not to scale

Published by Castleberg, 18 Yealand Ave., Giggleswick,
Settle, North Yorkshire, BD24 0AY

Typeset in Goudy medium and printed by J W Lambert & Sons, Station Road,
Settle, North Yorkshire, BD24 9AA

ISBN: 1 871064 70 8

Contents

Illustrations

The co-operation of British Rail Eastern Region Photographic Unit is warmly acknowledged. BR photographs by Robert Anderson.

Drawings by Peter Fox. Those of engineering details of Ribblehead viaduct have been based (with permission) on British Rail documents. The map is a sketch only and is not to scale. Peter Fox also supplied the following photographs: 42 (bottom), 46 (bottom), 47, 71 (top and centre), 82.

Photograph on page 47 — Richard Hughes.
Drawing on page 12 by Geoff Bounds.
Drawing of shanty town on page 34 (bottom) — R Lindup.
Map on page 16 and detail from conveyance — courtesy of Dr J A Farrer.

Foreword

THE Settle-Carlisle railway has an almost indefinable magic—a cocktail mix of fact and folklore, acquired over more than 100 years of operation on the high and remote Pennines. It is one of the best-known and best-loved pieces of railway in Britain, if not the world.

Not surprisingly, this magic has wrapped itself around the line's most famous viaduct, Ribblehead, which strides across the head of Chapel-le-Dale, buffeted by wind, rain and extremes of temperature.

With a length of 400 yards, and standing a little over 100 ft in height, Ribblehead is the longest viaduct on this railway. It is not the highest and, indeed, in its construction and vital statistics it has no claim to being unique in the realm of viaducts on the British rail system.

What makes Ribblehead truly fascinating is the story of its construction, the rumbustuous life in the shanty towns on Batty Moss and adjacent areas, and also the often harsh weather. Few viaducts have fostered so many stories about the effects of the elements as this great and isolated structure.

To have been the Project Manager during the time of the repair works, with the exception of the 1988 trial repairs, has been a great privilege. As I looked at the viaduct in April, 1992, when it was bathed in Spring sunshine, it was satisfying to sense that Ribblehead, a scheduled Ancient Monument and a living part of the nation's heritage, had been restored, as closely as possible to its original condition, and that so many people

7

had worked so hard towards this end.

The re-birth of Ribblehead also owes much to those organisations who have given generously in terms of grants and other contributions, some big, some small. The provision of grant-finding to the level enjoyed by Ribblehead has meant that the work could be completed without interruption, save for a planned winter shutdown.

It is a particular source of satisfaction to any Project Manager when such work is complete on time and to cost. At Ribblehead, many possibilities existed for delay and disruption, but none of the problems which were thrown at us was incapable of resolution. The knowledge gained in methods of repair will prove invaluable when considering work on some other viaducts on the Settle-Carlisle line.

Herein lies a warning. The Settle-Carlisle has a number of great viaducts. The restoration of Ribblehead marks the end of the beginning. As far as the remaining viaducts are concerned, considerable repairs will have to be undertaken to give these, and the Settle-Carlisle, an infrastructure basis that is sound and on which the railway will be capable of meeting the needs of the 21st century.

GEOFF BOUNDS

Introduction

REFLECTING on the last few years, it is clear to me that very few of the people who have been closely involved in the Ribblehead project have failed to be captivated by the splendid viaduct. This has converted the restoration work into a labour of love.

Ribblehead viaduct has long had a special importance as the "flagship of the line". However, as resident engineer, I am conscious also of the morale-boosting effect that has sprung from the interest and goodwill of the public. The encouragement of many people has stimulated all those concerned with the restoration to give their very best efforts to the work.

I was delighted when, in early June, 1988, I was entrusted with the supervision of trial repair works at Ribblehead. I admired the work of the Victorian railway engineers in a special way, having been for over 20 years the most northerly resident engineer of the former Midland Region.

The Settle-Carlisle was within easy reach of my home station at Lancaster. I saw Ribblehead viaduct during leisuretime walks on the Three Peaks, though my work had not taken me to this stretch of the line. Instead, I had been concerned, in 1978-79, with the construction of the rail bridge over the Appleby by-pass.

At that time, the fate of the line seemed inextricably linked with the fate of Ribblehead, which appeared to be in such rapid structural deterioration that major repairs or even a complete renewal would soon become necessary.

The years passed. More costly solutions were put forward to solve the viaduct's troubles, against a background of a decreasing amount of traffic on the Settle-Carlisle. I avidly followed news of the line's varying fortunes. We all had rising hopes as a trial repair scheme was announced.

As a member of the team involved in the trial, I will long remember the summer of 1988. It was an exciting time. Much depended on the outcome of our inquiries and work. The fate of the line could be decided by our assessment of the physical condition of the old structure and on our estimates of the cost of restoration.

The trial ended successfully, with the refurbishment of two piers and an arch. Much knowledge was gained which could be used to prepare the main structural repair scheme. Reports of the engineers and quantity surveyors, issued when the works were concluded, showed that the anticipated costs of the full restoration would be much less than anticipated—facts which doubtless helped towards the eventual reprieve of the line from closure, an announcement which came in 1989.

The main repair works began in the summer of 1990 and were completed early in 1992. Thus ended a challenging and enjoyable project.

Those who look at Ribblehead today see a structure with an appearance similar to that when it was completed in 1876. I am confident that the viaduct will withstand the ravages of the High Pennine weather. The data and experience gained at Ribblehead will be invaluable on other restoration projects at the great viaducts of the Settle-Carlisle.

A P FRESCHINI

In Praise of the Settle-Carlisle Railway

THE RAILWAY is distinguished by its straightness. It meant to get to Scotland in the fastest possible time and would brook no delays. If a hill got in the way, the Settle-Carlisle went straight through it—either by tunnel or cutting...Its viaducts are titanic examples of Victorian architecture, built by men who clearly believed that while the impossible might take a little longer it had better not take too long!

Yorkshire Life (1976)

RIBBLEHEAD VIADUCT, absolutely alone in a wilderness of rough windblown moorland, with 2,414 ft Whernside as a backcloth, is one of the most dramatically situated engineering works in England...

Peter E Baughan, Centenary of the Long Drag (1976)

I STARTED to explore the country north of Skipton and discovered the rural charms of places like Bell Busk; the rugged splendours and impressive loneliness of Ribblesdale with its three peaks, its potholes and rushing waters; the placid beauty of Dentdale; the magnificence of Wild Boar Fell dominating Ais Gill and the kindness of the Eden Valley. And through it all there ran the most marvellous railway which seemed as much at home as the rocks and rivers.

Eric Treacy, in a foreword to Rails in the Fells (1973)

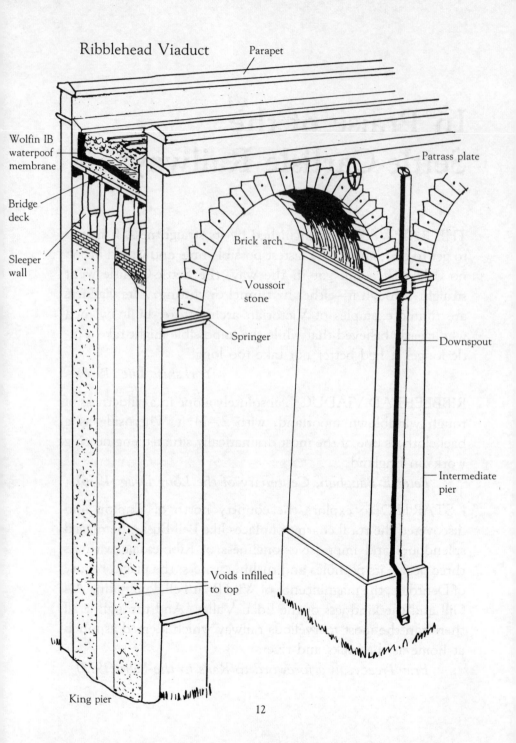

Ribblehead Viaduct

Parapet

Wolfin IB waterpoof membrane

Patrass plate

Bridge deck

Brick arch

Sleeper wall

Voussoir stone

Springer

Downspout

Intermediate pier

Voids infilled to top

King pier

12

1: The High Arches

RIBBLEHEAD viaduct is so much a part of the landscape that what is ordinary in engineering terms has become extraordinary in this High Pennine setting.

When the first snow of winter has dusted the northern fells, a traveller who has traversed Ribblesdale faces the sudden thrilling prospect of a 24-arch limestone viaduct set against a backdrop of white-capped Whernside, the highest peak in the Yorkshire Dales National Park.

The appearance of the viaduct changes by the minute. A line of lofty piers offers a bold pattern of sunshine and shadow. Variations are provided by the seasons and by the transient weather—"the Ribblehead factor" in engineering projects: often a Pennine cocktail of driving rain, wind and mist.

Ribblehead viaduct stands at the meeting place of several valleys, where all the winds are at home. Set well back from a road, and built on a curve, this stupendous piece of Victorian railway engineering differs strikingly in appearance according to the direction from which it is approached.

View it from the Ingleton road, and it appears to be compressed, with the piers almost touching each other. Viewed from the east, especially at sundown, and the viaduct forms a purple pattern against the setting sun, stretching out across the head of Chapel-le-Dale as though trying to tickle the ribs of Ingleborough and Whernside.

A structure that appears graceful and slender from a distance, such as from one of the little farms on the flanks of Whernside, is awesome in its immensity at close quarters. An unmetalled track which begins near the *Station Hotel* passes under one of the high arches. The limestone piers rise to a maximum height of 104 feet and carry the Settle-Carlisle line across the valley for no less than a quarter of a mile.

This was to be the largest visible structure in the Midland Railway Company's bold venture to drive a railway between Settle and Carlisle by the fell-top route linking the north-south valleys of Ribble and Eden. A writer in the *Carlisle Patriot*, at the time the railway was opened, referred to "a continued succession of high hills with intervening valleys, so that the line is alternately carried over viaducts or through tunnels or under hills hundreds of feet in height".

In its remote, windswept location, Ribblehead is buffeted by high winds and soaked by rain which, though averaging 70 inches a year, has occasionally exceeded 100", as testified by the rain gauge used at Ribblehead station in the 1950s. The gauge recorded 109½" in 1954 and 5.2" fell on a single day, December 2, 1954.

The prevailing westerly winds sweeping across Morecambe Bay and up the Lune Valley are funnelled between limestone scars in Chapel-le-Dale and their first major obstacle is Ribblehead viaduct.

Work on the viaduct began in 1870 and proceeded with the boldness and courage which Victorian railway builders had in abundance. Yet Midland Railway Company records hint at desperation. In those inflationary timers, the *Midland*—young and thrustful—was overstretching itself.

In the Settle-Carlisle project, the *Midland* was having to build a railway it did not really want now that its arch-rival, the *London and North Western*, had got off its high-horse and was prepared to co-operate more fully with regard to passenger and goods traffic to Scotland.

The Settle-Carlisle Railway sprang from inter-company rivalry. So unsatisfactory had the arrangement between the two companies been that the Midland introduced a Bill to enable it to reach Scotland on its own metals. With greater goodwill available, an Abandonment Bill was applied for—and thrown out by Parliament.

All the *Midland* could do was gulp, dust down the old files and put out the contracts to tender. Ribblehead viaduct (originally named Batty Green from its location) came under Contract No 1 and was in course of construction for five years.

Today, almost 120 years after the last coping of the parapet was slipped into place and regular goods and passenger services were inaugurated, the viaduct, having been restored, looks as smart as it did in the construction period. It epitomises the spirit and sturdy character of the most famous railway in England.

RIBBLEHEAD RE-BORN is published to commemorate the completion of that £3 million restoration project. It tells the story of the viaduct's design, construction and maintenance. It gives a detailed account, from an engineering point of view, of the restoration.

It is, indeed, the definitive account of an outstanding Victorian railway structure.

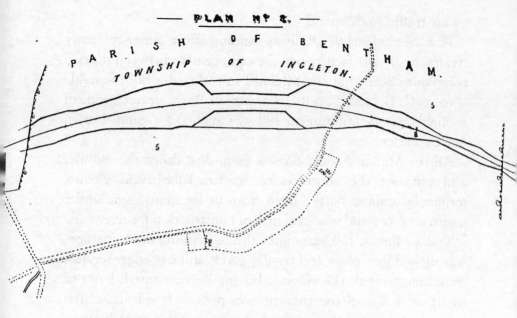

PARISH OF BENTHAM.

TOWNSHIP OF INGLETON.

The drawing (above) is from the documentation when the Midland Railway Company negotiated the purchase of land at Ribblehead from the Farrer family, of Clapham. Rights which Parliament granted must then be secured "on the ground" by legal processes. The map clearly shows the shape of the proposed viaduct and attendant embankments. Crossley, the Chief Engineer, was not sure, until the last moment, how many arches there would be. Much depended on the availability of masons to do the work. In the end, 24 arches were created.

2: In the Beginning

IN ITS northward progress, during which it absorbed several lesser companies, the *Midland* reached Ingleton where its Scottish traffic had to be put in the hands of its rival, the LNER.

James Allport, the *Midland's* general manager, determined that the company would go to Scotland on its own metals. He complained, in anguish: "I have been by fast train from Derby to Ingleton, and then been attached to six or eight coal trucks to be carried on to Tebay".

The means chosen by the *Midland* was to come to an agreement with the promoters of a North of England Union Railway, who in 1865 had introduced a Bill to Parliament to construct a line from Settle to Hawes. The *Midland* reached an agreement to re-introduce this Bill as a Settle to Carlisle railway, with a branch to Hawes. The Act was obtained in 1866.

The *Midland* line was envisaged as a finely engineered, all-weather route using viaducts and tunnels to provide a fast ride to and from the Border City. What matter if this line, at 72 miles, was some 24 miles longer than the Ingleton-Carlisle route, via Lowgill?

As related, the *London and North Western* offered better mutual working arrangements and a relieved *Midland* applied unsuccessfully for an Abandonment.

On Site

A practical route for the railway was worked out when, in 1865, James Allport and John Crossley, the engineer-in-chief, went "prospecting", as they called it. These two men walked most of the way between Settle and Carlisle.

Charles Stanley Sharland, a young Tasmanian, a member of Crossley's staff, was the engineer entrusted with the task of surveying the route. He and his tiny support team made their way southwards from Carlisle, taking flying levels, and in due course they plotted on the map the course of the line.

It would take advantage of two north-south valleys (the Eden and upper Ribble) and a practical way was found across the high spurs of the Pennines, where there was a sometimes bewildering alternation of small dales and gills [water-carved valleys].

A tunnel would be driven through Blea Moor, at one point having a depth of 500 feet from the surface. At Batty Green, where Chapel-le-Dale, Littledale and North Ribblesdale met, embankments and a substantial viaduct would be needed.

During September, 1866, Crossley staked out sections of the route as necessary before the onset of the Pennine winter. A morose farmer said to the *Midland* men that there was not a level piece of ground large enough to build a house upon between Settle and Carlisle.

In the hill country, a farmer suggested that in view of the undulating nature of the ground, the railway would have to be built on stilts. He was not far wrong. Just north of Ribblehead, high-soaring viaducts were needed at Dent Head, Arten Gill and Dandry Mire.

The land at Ribblehead was purchased from the Farrer family, whose Ingleborough Estate stretched from Clapham over the mountain of that name and included Blea Moor. Contract

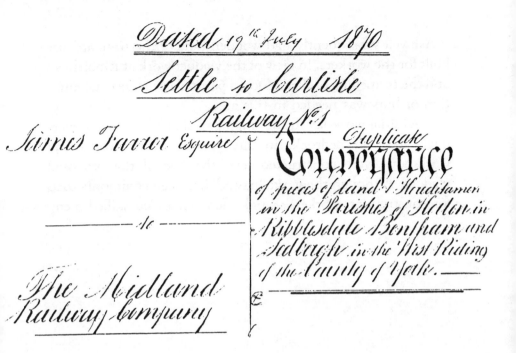

Dated 19th July 1870

Settle to Carlisle Railway No. 1

James Farrar Esquire

to

The Midland Railway Company

Duplicate

Conveyance of pieces of land & Hereditament in the Parishes of Hilton in Ribblesdale Bentham and Sedbergh in the West Riding of the County of York.

No. 1 (17¼ miles from Settle to just north of Dent Head) was awarded to John Ashwell, of Kentish Town, North London, who appointed Edgar O Ferguson as his resident engineer.

The construction of the viaduct would be managed by Charles and Walter Hirst, who mustered a workforce of 60 or more masons and labourers. (One of the Hirst brothers died and his ornate tombstone can be seen just inside the yard at Chapel-le-Dale church).

The first party of resident engineers and their men arrived at Ribblehead in the autumn of 1869, their living quarters being a wooden caravan, brought from London behind a traction engine and parked just off the old turnpike road.

Ashwell subsequently had wooden huts of the standard size built for the workers. In view of the viaduct work at Ribblehead and the tunnelling of Blea Moor, a particularly large concentration of huts was needed in this area.

The initial work lay in the sinking of shafts so that the piers might rest on bedrock. In due course, a brickworks and workshops were constructed near the line of the proposed viaduct. Although the word "navvy" has been commonly used for construction workers, Ribblehead demanded skilled men.

3: Life at Ribblehead

THE Settle-Carlisle railway was among the last to be constructed using a huge labour force, in this case some 6,000 men spread along the 72 miles, with concentrations in such areas as Batty Green (Ribblehead), where the major works included the viaduct and Blea Moor tunnel. Mr Ashwell, the contractor, had to put £20,000 of plant on the site before the work could begin. Most of it was brought via Ingleton. Local people were soon complaining about the state of the dale road, which in those days was not macadamed.

The first party of engineers and workmen arrived at Ribblehead in the autumn of 1869. Their quarters were one of the four-wheeled caravans as used by roadmen. The view was mainly of moss and moor, with Whernside bonneted with cloud. From their constricted quarters, the men set off to determine where the piers of Ribblehead viaduct (originally called Batty Moss viaduct) would rest. They made experimental borings through the moss, questing for rock.

They doubtless heard the story of Batty Wife Hole, a pothole with standing water, where a Mrs Batty is said to have done the weekly wash. By the time the railway works were completed, Mrs Batty had to look elsewhere, for the hole was filled in.

In the 1870s, the highway up Chapel-le-Dale to Ribblehead and Hawes carried little traffic beyond farmers in their horse-drawn traps and tradesmen with carts. In "railway time", the whole area became alive with workers, their families and lodgers, as also with tradesmen of various kinds.

It was rather like an upshot frontier town in America during the drive to conquer the West. A vehicle with hooped top covered with canvas, and not unlike one of the wagons used in America, was to be seen at Ribblehead, where it served as an ambulance.

The wet autumn of 1869 was followed by a bitterly cold winter, during which snow lay on the backs of the hill sheep for two months and, to quote a workman, "many on 'em frozen as hard as a chip". Even less favoured than the surveyors at Ribblehead were those engaged in driving levels and shafts to excavate a long tunnel through Blea Moor. They lived in tents for a while and moved their equipment and provisions on the backs of donkeys.

Meanwhile, where Ribblehead viaduct now stands, Mr Ashwell the contractor laid out a workyard with a number of service units—a blacksmith's shop, saw mill, carpenter's shed, stables, pay office and stores. Here, too, was the Sebastopol brickworks, the largest of the structures, breathing dark smoke into the thin mountain air. In February, 1871, the manager, Mr Rixon, lost his wife to a dark-haired navvy. They eloped and were pursued as far as Skipton, when the trail went cold.

The contractor needed steam power to move stone from Littledale to the viaduct and bricks from Ribblehead to the tops of the shafts on Blea Moor. A locomotive was drawn up Storrs Brow at Ingleton by a large team of horses. Then, with fewer horses in attendance, it was moved along the deeply-rutted dale road to Batty Green. Here it was used to haul open wagons on two and a-half miles of tramway on the laying of which the men "worked like Yankees" and built the iron-road at the rate of nearly a mile a week.

Eventually, the tramway was extended to four miles of track, enabling stone, mortar and other materials to be moved to the site of the viaduct. Coal and bricks were taken to Blea Moor. Coal powered the locomotive and also the stationery steam engines situated at the head of the shafts, which were used for sending down men, provisions and explosives and for raising the vast amount of displaced rock, which was tipped on the moor.

Batty Green, the main hutment, lay around the junction of the Ribblesdale road with the Ingleton-Hawes road. Not far from Batty Green was a "posh" suburb known as Belgravia, where there were porches on the huts. Near the course of the line were hutments named Sebastopol and Inkermann, after places that became well-known during the Crimean War. Some of the workmen had been engaged in building a railway line along which supplies were transported from the ships to the men in the front line. Towards Blea Moor were the huts known as Jericho and Jerusalem. On Blea Moor itself the temporary settlement had a prosaic title—Tunnel Huts.

Most of the workforce were English. Of the Irish, some who had worked on the Mersey docks were called "Liverpool Irishmen". An English labourer was taken to court because on three occasions he had been heard threatening to burn down an Irishman's hut.

Such a conurbation, where the population at its peak was around 1,500 souls, needed a well organised supply system for food and drink. The railway historian Williams mentioned the arrival at Batty Green of carts owned by milkmen, greengrocers, butchers, bakers, brewers and numerous hawkers.

One firm which grew rapidly in size and wealth during the construction period was Messrs Burgoyne and Cocks, of Settle and Batty Green; they supplied foodstuffs through several shops, three of which had been opened at Ribblehead and Blea

Moor.

Settle was the place where this enterprising firm, using two large ovens, baked 4,000 loaves a day. Next door, they "butched" each week four fat cows and from 10 to 15 sheep, besides "porklings and fat pigs". The partners distributed newspapers and periodicals.

It was not all profit. When sending a consignment of food from Batty Green to Blea Moor, the wagon toppled over into the aforementioned ravine, where it was pilfered, the loss to Burgoyne and Cocks being valued at £16.

A hospital was established on a small knoll near the road junction at Batty Green. Two detached huts were connected by a covered way. There were beds for 20 patients. In the summer of 1871, a case of smallpox was moved from Ingleton to Batty Green. In the following month, 35 cases were admitted and of these 19 were cured and discharged and only three had died.

The dead were borne reverently down the dale to tiny St Leonard's church, where about 200 people—men, women and some children—were buried in "railway time". So many interments took place, the churchyard had to be extended.

That was over 120 years ago. It was noticeable during the recent restoration of Ribblehead viaduct that few of the modern workers stayed close to their work. Lodgings were found at Ingleton. Some men commuted between home and workplace in their cars.

4: An Elegant Structure

RIBBLEHEAD was founded on rock. The original drawings indicate a solid limestone footing. Grey and weathered, like the natural outcrops about it, the viaduct has become a part of the landscape of the Three Peaks Country.

The viaduct was constructed to a well-tested design approved by John Crossley, the engineer, who had delayed his retirement to see the Settle-Carlisle through to completion. Not until the end of 1872 did the Construction Committee make up its mind about the dimensions of the viaduct or the number of arches to be built.

The decision was based on the availability of labour. If there had been a preponderance of navvies, the embankments would have been extended, leaving space for 18 arches. In the event, sufficient masons were found and 24 arches resulted, the maximum height being 104 ft and the structure having a length of 440 yards.

Non-local material for Ribblehead was brought in by rail to Ingleton and then transported by horse and cart along the old turnpike road through Chapel-le-Dale, a road which was soon deeply-rutted and a quagmire in wet weather.

Ribblehead is a composite structure, the masonry being of stone with the arches turned in brick. Blocks for the masonry were quarried nearby and bricks were made on site.

The Ground

Accounts of the construction period tell of sodden conditions at the head of Ribblesdale. On either side of the viaduct are large numbers of "swallow-holes", green-sided funnels caused by the seepage of clay through cracks in the underlying limestone.

The bogs were negotiated with the help of an agricultural cart consisting of a large barrel on a light frame, with shafts for a horse. This "bog cart" ran easily over soft ground. On one occasion, a floundering horse had the shoes ripped from its feet. Another broke a leg and had to be shot.

Contemporary accounts tell of miry conditions. When the engineer's caravan arrived in 1869, a man stood at the door when darkness fell and, using a bull's eye lantern, guided the men across the boggy ground.

During the winter of 1872-3, a visitor to Batty Green saw the navvies returning from work, noting that "the face of the swamp in the watery twilight was alive with navvies...They stalked carelessly through the most horrid clinging mire."

Such accounts imply that the Ribblehead of the 1870s was even wetter than that of the 1990s.

A year elapsed between the arrival of the first group of engineers and the excavation of a shaft for Pier No. 13, the first pier to be tackled. Construction of Ribblehead viaduct began in the middle presumably because of uncertainty about the number of piers to be built.

In the early summer of 1871, wooden staging was being erected for the first group of piers. A photograph of the construction period shows a thick coverlet of peat and heather on the adjacent land.

The Footings

The bedrock was exposed following the removal of up to 25 ft of glacial clay and peat. Working drawings of the footings indicate variations in level from one to another, these being due to the shelving or fragmentation of the underlying limestone.

The bases of piers rest on concrete, enabling the piers to commence from a level base. The most northerly six piers were the first to be constructed and the viaduct was designed in groups of six, with intervening king-piers that are double the width.

The Stone

The contractor told FS Williams, the *Midland* Company's historian, who toured the railway works, that a considerable search was made for a quarry and several trial holes were sunk. The best source lay beneath the bed of a stream in Littledale, one and a-quarter miles from the viaduct. Further good quality limestone was removed from the lineside scars between Ribblehead and Selside.

Pieces weighing up to eight tons each were quarried. The limestone varied in quality, the evidence suggesting that stone lying nearest the surface was of the poorest quality.

The limestone is hard, dark and fine-grained. Natural defects have become more evident over the years and some stones have reverted to a shaly type of material. Bands of shale and softer silty material in many stones speeded up the effects normally caused by weathering. The presence of many of the weaknesses now visible would not have been so apparent to those who built Ribblehead viaduct as they selected suitable masonry.

Where good stone was selected, it has remained good, being extremely hard, ringing like a bell when hit. Other stone has weathered badly, its surface becoming friable and crumbly.

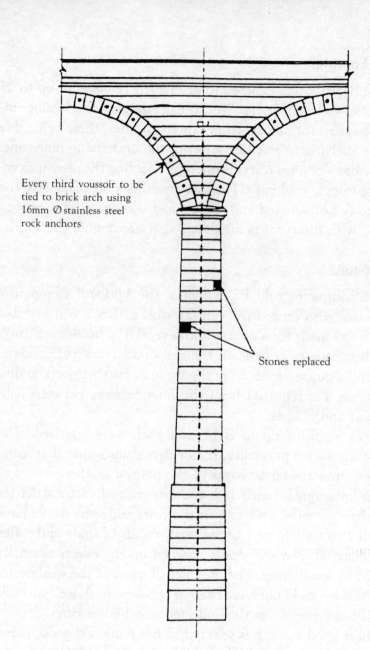

Every third voussoir to be
tied to brick arch using
16mm ∅ stainless steel
rock anchors

Stones replaced

Typical intermediate pier

(West elevation — East elevation similar)

28

Limestone for Ribblehead was blasted from its native beds and conveyed on narrow gauge tramways to the vicinity of the viaduct. Here it was dressed prior to being added to the piers. Dynamite (a novelty, costing £200 a ton) was the explosive used. Its effects were little known but it was less kindly to rock than gunpowder. Consequently fine cracks appeared in the blocks—cracks which would expand during hand-dressing.

The Piers

When the embankment to the north of the viaduct had been completed, the contractor was able to lay rails and operate a steam crane, the rails extending on to the wooden scaffolding of the first group of piers and arches.

According to dates written on the original working drawings, the construction work began in the autumn of 1870 on the foundations to Piers 13, 14 and 15. Thereafter, work on the structure was from north to south, the design permitting the construction of four independent groups of six arches.

The ordinary piers are slender in appearance with an external elevation of 12' wide at the base, tapering to 6' 3" wide at the springer.

These piers are rectangular, with an external skin of dressed masonry blocks of differing lengths and widths but laid in regular courses of varying depths. The corners of the piers are generally formed of the largest blocks.

Internally, the line of the masonry is much less regular, following the varying thicknesses of the individual facing blocks. The centre of a pier is filled with irregularly shaped, though similarly sized, pieces of limestone.

Voids between the stones were packed with sand (in a few places with mortar), the quality varying. In some piers it was poorly consolidated, the central core being loose and voided.

A king-pier (every sixth pier) has two voids up the middle, each void having an area of 7' 6" x 8' 6". Such a pier consists of almost three times the surface area of a normal pier. King-piers were designed to be able to resist the thrust from the adjacent flights of six arches, thus reducing the need to support all 24 arches at the same time during construction.

By including these stiffening piers at intervals, it was ensured that if an arch was lost only six would suffer from the domino effect of a falling arch taking with it all the others.

The Arches

Bricks used for the arches were laid in independent rings, tied together at regular intervals for additional strength. The arches vary from 2' 3" thick at the crown to 3' thick at the springing points.

Masonry voussoirs completed the external ends of the arches, maintaining the viaduct's stylish appearance. The first group of six piers on the northern side were made ready for arching by 1872. A year later, 100 men had completed 12 arches. The span between the piers was 45' and it was claimed that when the wooden framing was removed, an arch dropped a mere quarter of an inch.

The brickworks built immediately to the east of the viaduct were intended to serve both the viaduct and Blea Moor tunnel, where a good deal of brick arching was needed.

One and a-half million bricks being needed for Ribblehead alone, a large plant was designed. A single oven had a capacity of from 14,000 to 15,000 bricks and firing them took a whole week. The brick-making clay was mixed with local shale.

These native bricks proved to be too porous to resist the freeze-thaw conditions of winter. Furthermore, the original bricks were riddled with foreign matter suggesting that control

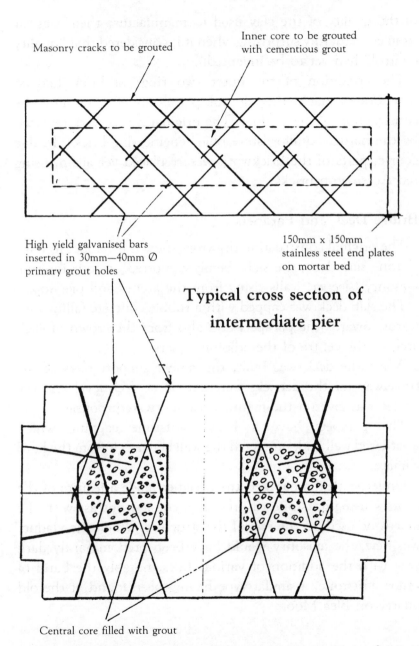

Masonry cracks to be grouted

Inner core to be grouted with cementious grout

High yield galvanised bars inserted in 30mm—40mm ⌀ primary grout holes

150mm x 150mm stainless steel end plates on mortar bed

Typical cross section of intermediate pier

Central core filled with grout

Typical cross section of king piers 6, 12 and 18

of the quality of the clay used to manufacture them was far from good (hardly surprising when it is considered that "quality control" had yet to be invented!).

The condition of the outer two rings of brick had so deteriorated that re-ringing took place only 40 years after the construction of the viaduct. The original bricks were replaced by the harder "Staffordshire blue" engineering bricks. In due course, parts of the brickwork were replaced yet again, using red Accrington bricks.

Bridge Deck and Parapets

The original construction drawings show the viaduct to have a stone slab deck, the slabs being supported on four internal masonry (sleeper) walls rising from the arches and pier tops.

The slab deck was capped with a rubble concrete falling out-wards towards the parapets and also from the crown of each arch to the centre of the adjoining piers.

When the deck was built, the timber support piers of the travelway for the derricks were cut off at deck level and the bridge was given a rudimentary asphalt waterproofing.

The parapets have a heavy gritstone capping which weathered well and, protected the wall beneath it from the hard climate.

Underneath the parapet, the designer made a feature of the courses using gritstone to provide a colour contrast with the limestone used on the rest of the structure. When the viaduct was new, the masonry would have been predominantly dark grey with the addition of various hues, notably the band of yellow gritstone, a similar type having been found at the old quarry on Blea Moor.

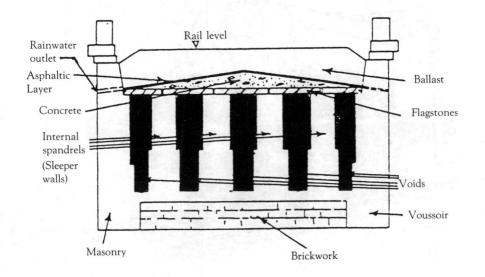

Rail level

Rainwater outlet

Asphaltic Layer

Concrete

Internal spandrels (Sleeper walls)

Ballast

Flagstones

Voids

Voussoir

Masonry

Brickwork

Cross section of original deck

Embankments

By the autumn of 1871, about 150,000 cubic yards of material had been removed south of Blea Moor in the making of cuttings. Most of this was dumped by gangs of men from Batty Green using tip wagons, to create the northern embankment of Ribblehead. Consequently, this is mainly of stone. The embankments were sown with ryegrass.

Above—Contractor's Locomotive of the 1870s.
Below—An artist's impression of the shanty life.

5: Under Pressure

THE 1870s found the *Midland* over-stretched and anxious. On the Continent there were wars and rumours of wars. Inflation was making nonsense of the original costings for the Settle-Carlisle.

The weather was generally inclement and the labour force fickle. Writing to his construction committee in April, 1871, John Crossley, engineer-in-chief, noted: "Good weather and men alone are wanted".

The effect of inclement weather had not been fully appreciated by John Crossley when he estimated the time and cost of the works. The construction period coincided with a particularly severe spell which included floods, blizzards and even a minor earthquake, which shook the huts on the flanks of Blea Moor, quite close to the viaduct.

That year began with a cold "snap" which halted all the work except that in the tunnels. Several months elapsed before the men began to drift back and, at Ribblehead, arrangements could be made for the scaffolding of the first batch of piers.

By August, heavy rain bogged down the workings. The men were on "short time" and many left for more lucrative work. The local men were inclined to stay off work for several weeks at haytime.

It was difficult to attract labour, which was now costing about 5s per day.

Work on Ribblehead viaduct continued on a shift system through some of the harshest winters of the 19th century, greatly affecting the morale of the labour force, who suffered great privation as they laboured in frost, snow, rain and gale. It was bound to affect the quality of the workmanship.

In October, the contractor William Ashwell, unable to meet his obligations because of steeply rising costs and the severity of the conditions on Contract No 1, was judged by the *Midland* to have been unfortunate. His contract was cancelled by amicable agreement, the Midland engineering staff taking over the work.

The summer of 1872 was notable for its incessant rainfall, the year's figure being almost double the 70″ average for Ribblehead. In November, the Midland's construction committee paid to the other contractors a 15 per cent bonus on agreed prices—if they undertook to push the work forward with all possible speed.

The Ingleton road to Ribblehead was in such a grim state that Crossley was joyful when he reported to his committee that, with the exception of one or two short stretches, a single railway line had been laid almost all the way from Settle to Ribblehead and would be useful for the transportation of goods that winter. He was proposing to cut the wages bill by weeding out indifferent workers.

In 1873, the piece-workers, whose pay structure had been improved, were inclined to leave work early on earning more than 6s for the day. Crossley wrote: "The day-men stay their hours but do not work to hurt themselves". The winter of 1873-4 was marked by flooding, followed by heavy falls of snow, once again bringing work almost to a standstill.

Crossley, worried and with his energies overtaxed, became ill at the close of 1874. Before he left, he had the pleasure of reporting that Contract No 1 had almost been completed.

The great engineer was succeeded by John Underwood and

in the following February, he was reporting on delays, some caused by the weather and others because of the unfriendly terrain.

Financial Matters

For the *Midland* Company, the Settle-Carlisle was a prime worry—a commitment to build a heavily engineered route it could ill afford. From the start, it was under financial pressure to complete the line quickly so that the restless shareholders might earn a dividend on traffic.

Added to worries over the escalating costs of building the line were contractural problems (as related, the contractor for Ribblehead ran out of money) and the usual difficulties of recruiting and holding labour.

It is not unlikely that the builders of such a large and expensive structure as Ribblehead "cut corners" where possible to reduce their costs. The variable condition of the infill to the piers, and the poor quality of the materials used within the parapet, supports the view that standards were allowed to slip.

Work up to the deck was completed by the close of 1873. Trains were crossing Ribblehead before the parapets were finally in place.

When the *Midland* Board met on February 22, 1876, E S Ellis, the chairman, said that the total cost of the line was expected to be £3,467,000.

6: Fact and Folklore

JOHN Ruskin, the distinguished Victorian thinker and art critic, travelled up Chapel-le-Dale on a breezy day and marvelled that the mountain Ingleborough managed to stand without rocking. The same degree of astonishment applies to Ribblehead viaduct as a westerly gale rampages through the district and moans through the arches with a sound like part of the sound-track of a Bronte film.

A hoary tale is told of the ganger who was crossing the viaduct when the wind blew away his cap, which was carried through an arch and dropped back on his head. The man was heard to comment that "t'wind might have made a better job of it, for it brought t'cap back wi' t'neb to one side."

It is an unlikely tale. The height of the Ribblehead parapets is such as to deflect the wind high above anyone crossing so that, to quote a former signalman at Blea Moor box, "thou could leet a pipe in calm weather when a gale was roaring' above thi head."

Ribblehead station had its moments. Derek Soames, signalman at Settle Junction, began as a boy porter and was sent to Ribblehead when one of the annual sheep sales was being held. Long trains of empty goods wagons were needed. If there was a strong wind it was capable of bringing such a train to a halt as it crossed the viaduct.

Normal goods trains had the wagon sheets stripped from them and scattered like autumn leaves. Eventually, men were mustered at the northern end of the viaduct for gale duty, their job being to tighten the ropes before the train crossed. They were also summoned at times of fog and snow.

Two world wars produced a crop of stories, including (from the 1939-45 war) the tale of a Home Guard unit mounting guard over the viaduct and using the station as a rallying point.

A man who was quite sure he had removed the bullets from his rifle at the end of a spell of duty tilted the gun upwards and pulled the trigger. There was a deafening bang and a bullet shot through the roof of the waiting room.

Jack Towler, ganger on the Ribblehead stretch in wartime, returned across the viaduct after working at Blea Moor at about 5 p.m. on a misty day. "We got as far as Ribblehead and heard a big aeroplane coming over, droning away." Jack said to one of his men: "He'll have to look out, the way he's going." The men did not get much further when "there was such a bang." A Lancaster bomber had crashed into Whernside.

Next morning, Jack looked through the staircase window at his home—one of the cottages at Salt Lake—and saw the remains of the huge plane spread-eagled on the fellside. The five crew members perished. Their bodies were reverently carried to Winterscales Farm and placed in the sitting room until they were claimed by the RAF.

When the Settle-Carlisle was blocked with snow, a viaduct like Ribblehead was a handy point at which to dispose of snow which had been loaded on to wagons. In 1947, snow was shovelled over the parapets by prisoners of war who had been brought up in ballast trains to do the work.

One of the train drivers shouted to Mrs Towler at Salt Lake, which had been isolated by road for weeks on end: "Do you want some black snow?" She had no idea what he was talking about but replied "yes". The man brought half a sack of coal. The Towlers, who had just had a pig slaughtered were able to respond with a gift of bacon.

The stationmaster at Ribblehead, attending to the paraffin lamps on the signals in windy weather, had to shield the flame while climbing a near vertical ladder. Sometimes, he had to repeat the process several times before the job was done.

The stationmaster also sent coded details of the weather to the Air Ministry to be incorporated in forecasts. If he was unsure about the height of the cloud base, the stationmaster released a balloon from one of the platforms and checked the rate of ascent.

In November, 1961, the Ribblehead anemometer recorded a wind speed of 92 miles an hour. A maintenance man on the viaduct reported that scaffolding planks "went up and down like piano keys".

Residents at the houses which stood beside the track near the south portal of Blea Moor regularly crossed the viaduct (unofficially) to entrain at Ribblehead for Settle on market day. Among them was Mrs William Davison, who told me that when her daughter was a babe in arms she carried the bairn across in fair weather and foul.

Mr Davison, a Methodist local preacher, when due to take a service at Dent, carried his bike through Blea Moor Tunnel and began to ride it on reaching the road at the other side.

With the appearance of a "shanty town" at the base of Ribblehead during the recent major restoration of Ribblehead viaduct, the folklore has been enlarged.

It now includes the story of the coffin, found standing upright in one of the refuges on the parapet at a double-width pier. A workman noticed that the coffin was of top quality and had a stainless steel plate inscribed "Walter". An arm was protruding from one side of the lid.

(continued on page 49)

Above: Ribblehead viaduct viewed from the east during the construction period. The most northerly seven arches have been turned. *Below:* Ribblehead during the restoration, May 1991.

Above—A Class 40 drawing a heavy goods train across Ribblehead, 1975. Heavy usage over many years was one of the reasons why the restoration of the viaduct was needed.

Below—Datestone on Ribblehead, painted and gilded at the completion of the Trial repairs, in the autumn of 1988.

This scaffolding was erected by a B R construction group around Pier 11, in 1975, to enable concrete cladding to be added.

The landscape qualities of three options to Ribblehead are shown by the use of this ingenious model made by British Rail in the late 1970s. The bottom picture shows the viaduct as it is.

Waterproofing the bridge deck in 1989.

Ribblehead during waterproofing. *Top:* A group of workmen well protected from wind and rain lay a textile fabric material to protect the waterproof membrane. *Below:* A group at the re-opening of the Settle-Carlisle after waterproofing.

A Royal visit
H R H The Duke of Gloucester at Ribblehead in June 1990. In the picture
are Peter Fox, Melanie Denley (resident engineer) and the Duke.

Winter at Ribblehead, November 1991. The winter proved to be relatively mild and work continued without a break to its conclusion in late January 1992.

The resident engineer was summoned. He estimated from the size of the coffin that three, maybe four, men would have been needed to carry it. He quickly deduced that the "arm" was made of rubber and that the screws holding down the lid were somewhat loose and could be easily turned. The coffin was empty. The police allowed it to be removed for disposal.

It was presumed that the coffin formed part of an elaborate hoax. In any case, as a local man said when he heard of the single, protruding arm: "It's 'armless".

A Small Settlement

The contractors' "shanty town" of modern times, unlike the hutments of the 1870s, had all "mod cons". The old huts were of wood and heated by a stove. The new buildings were Portakabins and Portaloos, each unit capable of being borne on the back of a lorry.

No record survives of the appearance of the office of a Victorian contractor or resident engineer at Ribblehead, so it was interesting to visit the office of Tony Freschini, the resident engineer, to see what he had accumulated.

The office walls were decorated with photo-copies of the original *Midland Railway* plans. Tony had been an engineer long enough to check them carefully, for Victorian engineers did not always work precisely according to plan.

A table in the office held cores taken from the viaduct. Here were cores of grey limestone from the piers and either red or blue brick from under the arches, obtained by means of a special diamond-tipped drill. Cores from bricks made of local materials at the time of construction were seen to be pitted with small holes and held particles of "foreign material".

The office was connected to the outer world by a telephone connected to the exchange at Ingleton. A postman regularly called in a red-painted Land Rover, the correspondence being addressed to "Ribblehead Viaduct, Ingleton, via Carnforth".

In the adjacent room, used for on-site discussions and to seat visiting worthies, stood a long table with chairs. Here, too, were plans, more cores of limestone and brick, plus a row of white safety helmets.

A Ribblehead hut, c1875, had a stove. The modern office was well-heated by an appliance running on oil. A small kitchen, complete with microwave cooker, brought some home comforts to one of the country's chilliest areas.

As in the old days, some of the workmen elected to live on site. Among them were the scaffolders. Their cabin had a rest room, kitchen and bedroom with four orthodox bunk beds and—to accommodate the extra two men—a two-decker bunk made of scaffolding and planks.

Leasing the Arches

In the midst of grave talk about the future role of Ribblehead viaduct came a startling declaration in the magazine *Railway World* for April—repeat April—1990, that British Rail was on the verge of completing a deal to lease the space within the arches.

The lessee, a recently-formed company called UK Reform, had been set up to operate private remand prisons under contract to the Home Office. The article was, of course, a hoax, but those who read it enjoyed an entertaining interlude in the Ribblehead story.

The privatisation of the remand service, responsible for prisoners before they went on trial, had been planned for some time. UK Reform was said to have been established by former senior prison service staff, with backing from three major insurance groups.

Ribblehead would be the first private prison to be built in Britain in modern times, occupying the spaces between the piers of Ribblehead viaduct. Each arch would be infilled from ground level to the crown of the arch, giving a self-contained block. The ground floor would be the administration and security level, with several floors of cells above it.

The cells would be on the west side of the structure, the space on the east being for stairways, access, sanitation and other requirements. A walled exercise yard would be made to the east of the viaduct, extending 50 yards from the structure.

It was recorded that agreement had been reached with the BR Property Board. Because Ribblehead is a listed structure, it was not possible (as originally proposed) to clad the whole structure in a cheerful modern material, such as yellow plastic panels. A compromise was reached. UK Reform would be planting Virginia creeper and honeysuckle to give the viaduct a more friendly aspect.

Account had been taken of the raised wind resistance of the structure once the arches were filled. The parapets were to be raised by 6 ft to protect trains from the extra force of the crosswinds forced to go over the viaduct.

Also, a special design of spring-loaded ventilator would be built into the new outer walls. Under gale force or stronger winds, this would open and allow some of the wind to pass through the cells and communal areas, keeping wind pressure on the viaduct within safety limits.

Here endeth an interlude of pure fantasy. . .

7: In Operation

WHEN the passenger service on the Settle-Carlisle line was inaugurated in 1876, the first train to cross Ribblehead was hauled by a green-painted engine designed by Matthew Kirtley, who had become locomotive superintendent of the *Midland* Railway in 1841, when he was 28 years of age. Kirtley died in 1873, but his designs had already taken practical shape.

On the day the line was opened for regular passenger traffic, Kirtley engine No. 806, driven by John Mayblin of Carlisle, crossed the viaduct from north to south and thus the *Midland* had its new direct route to Scotland using coaches of a new type which gave passengers a comfortable ride.

At Ribblehead, the farmfolk stared with drooping lower jaws as the double-headed Kirtleys hauled "the celebrated Pullman Cars". Passengers from London to Scotland could "retire to rest at one terminus and alight refreshed at the other in the morning".

Although *Midland* pride in its rolling stock continued, the Pullmans were not popular and were soon replaced. The two main complaints were that they were draughty and lacked the compartments demanded by Victorian conservatism.

Not until 1892 were dining cars introduced. Yet cold luncheon baskets were available (at 3s or 15p) at selected stations. A passenger who acquired one when the northbound trains stopped at Hellifield was doubtless still munching as he or she gazed out over the parapets of Ribblehead, a basket containing half a chicken with ham or tongue, salad, cheese, butter and a half bottle of burgundy claret, stout, apollinaris or a bottle of aerated water.

The change of livery from green to red came in 1880 and the famous "Derby red" was chosen in 1883 and remained in use until the 1939-45 war.

Kirtley's successor, Samuel Johnson, brought in heavier stock—without substantially increasing operating costs—supervising a change on the Settle-Carlisle to compounding. His 4-4-0s, in various guises, were also built by his successor, Richard Deeley, and handled most of the traffic across Ribblehead viaduct until the 1930s, when the Staniers appeared.

8: Trial and Restoration

THE remorseless natural erosion caused by wind, rain, frost and thaw led to subtle changes to the appearance of Ribblehead viaduct—to the flaking and cracking of stones. Less obvious were deficiencies in the Victorian workmanship and the stresses brought about by heavier trains.

Even before the 1914-18 war, the piers of Ribblehead were swathed with wooden scaffolding. Men worked on the re-bricking of the arches as traffic rumbled overhead.

The old-time scaffolders needed brawn as well as brains according to an account given to me by Harry Cox, of Settle, who between 1905 and 1910 helped to re-brick the most northerly eight arches in the traditional way, operating from timber scaffolding, with wooden floors set under the arches on which the men could work with safety.

The job lasted for several summers. Harry recalled: "We used a crab [hand-operated winch] to draw up lengths of scaffolding, ten poles to each pier. Each pole was about 20 feet long." Using the crab, a baulk some 40 feet long was raised to fit from corbel to corbel, where it was wedged with iron padlocks.

Other baulks were fitted to provide a firm foundation for the battens which fitted side by side to make a floor on which the brickies worked.

In due course, three floors were positioned and held firmly by struts and pillars.

For all the massiveness of its construction, and the boldness of Victorian vision that placed a viaduct in this wild spot, Ribblehead viaduct was in constant need of attention. The engineers carrying out their regular visual checks saw an increasing number of deficiencies in blocks, a natural consequence of the exposure of this type of material to stress and the weather. The Settle-Carlisle carried a heavy tonnage of both passenger and freight traffic until the mid-1970s.

By the early 1980s, Ribblehead was an ailing giant. Several of the piers were strapped with "girdles" of old bull-head rail and one pier had reinforced concrete corners. A visitor might also have noticed that some of the seemingly invincible limestone blocks were cracked from top to bottom and that after heavy rain, water spurted from some of the joints in the piers.

The Regional Civil Engineer asked for comments on how the regular major expense of maintaining Ribblehead might be avoided. The replacement of the viaduct was considered and proposals were drawn up for several options. When an embankment was suggested, the idea was quickly discarded, for Ribblehead had been scheduled as an ancient monument. Whatever happened, it would have to be preserved.

A reminder of this inquiry of the late 1970s is an ingenious model made to assess the effect on the landscape of the optional structures. The BR modellers fitted a representation of the district and the existing viaduct into a glass-fronted case. The viaduct could be slipped out to be replaced by models of the optional structures, including modern concrete bridges. This model impressed the director of the National Railway Museum at York.

British Rail, faced with the potentially enormous cost of repairing the viaduct at a time of declining freight traffic, also considered alternative routes for passenger traffic. In 1983, it was decided that the Settle-Carlisle would be closed, a proposal that was fought tooth and nail in a long campaign which has been fully documented elsewhere.

When the government reprieved the Settle-Carlisle, BR (like the *Midland* at the time when its abandonment bill was rejected) had to accept the Parliamentary decision with good grace. And those who had done their best to baulk BR now turned their attention to helping to make the line pay through publicity and voluntary work.

A Scheme of Repairs

Throughout their campaign, the objectors had been concerned at the wide variations in the BR estimates of the cost of repairing Ribblehead viaduct. It was felt by such as the Friends of the Settle-Carlisle that probable costs had been exaggerated in order to improve the case for closure.

Little known at that time was the extent of the investigatory work carried out by BR, who were anxious to understand why the viaduct was in rapid deterioration. Structural tests and surveys by independent experts and the BR Research Department, over several years, reflected official concern and a desire to understand and then cure the problem.

Because the results of these tests were inconclusive, estimates of the cost of repair varied widely. So did opinions on the condition of the structure and the extent of the repairs needed if it was restored to a standard acceptable for the foreseeable pattern of rail traffic.

Consequently, and with the government now intent on privatising the Settle-Carlisle, the General Manager asked the London Midland Region Chief Civil Engineer to develop a suitable scheme of repairs which must be accurately costed.

The Engineers took into account such matters as:

1. Had Ribblehead been built in accordance with the original drawings? (This is not always the case with old structures but

it would be of great importance when considering the structural behaviour of the viaduct).

2. Was the degree of delapidation—so clearly visible on the outside of the structure—symptomatic of more serious hidden problems or was it merely superficial?

3. Would major repairs be required to the deck? (It had long been recognised that the deck would need reproofing, since water was seeping through all the arches. The structural integrity of the deck was also questionable since there had been a history of minor losses of ballast into the spandrel voids following localised slab failures).

4. How much work would be needed to restore the brickwork at the interface with the masonry voussoir?

5. Why was there severe cracking in the masonry blocks at the corners of many piers? (Evidence from previous repair works indicated that the infill to the piers was, in some cases, less than satisfactory. A means would have to be found to improve this).

From their experiences with similar structures elsewhere, the engineers were able to prepare a trial scheme of repairs designed to answer the important questions.

A contract for the trial was drawn up in a flexible manner so that changes might be made as knowledge was gained about Ribblehead. The works, undertaken in 1988, consisted of the repair of king-pier No.12, intermediate pier No.13 and the associated arch. The area of deck between the two piers was waterproofed.

The trial repairs were completed in 14 weeks at a cost of £380,000. The Engineer's report estimated £3 million as the likely cost for repairing the whole viaduct.

The Engineer was relieved to note that the state of some of the principal parts of the viaduct was better than had been feared. Expensive major works were unlikely. Happily, the viaduct had been constructed in reasonable conformity with the drawings.

The trial revealed features of the original construction not previously recorded, such as the series of square holes at regular intervals and in a regular pattern on the deck over each pier, to which reference has already been made.

Some holes contained remnants of substantial timberwork, indicating that when the construction was complete the timber support piers of the travelway for the derricks were cut off at deck level prior to the bridge being given an asphalt water-proofing.

A century of Pennine rainfall, filtering through the track ballast, had rotted the timber stumps, allowing water to enter the spandrel voids and piers. Such water leeched between limestone blocks, washing away the mortar and sand infill. The structure was now vulnerable to the effect of driving rain and to the fast freeze-thaw process of winter. This process also worsened cracks in the limestone blocks.

The Engineers were able to examine in detail the fracture bet-ween the stone face of the structure and the brick in the arches brought about by the differential stiffness of the two materials and also from heavy train loadings on to the parapets. As ex-pected, cracks were found between those two materials at the "tail" of the voussoir stones.

This factor, considered in relation to the heavy freight and passenger trains using the Settle-Carlisle until the late 1970s, explains why Ribblehead had become progressively more fes-tooned with patresse plates, associated with steel tie bars pass-ing from one side of the viaduct to the other to stabilise the spandrel walls.

The trial repairs of 1988 ended with the re-gilding of the numbers on the datestone. The restoration work had taken place against a background of governmental plans for its sale. It was reckoned that no one would be interested in buying Ribblehead viaduct unless the cost of outstanding repairs could be quantified. At long last, the Engineers had some worth-while information about the structure.

While the threat of a sale hung over the line, and as long as traffic was declining, British Rail did not feel justified in carrying out a full restoration. The governmental decision in April 1989, to refuse British Rail's application to close the Settle-Carlisle led BR into making a sudden U-turn.

Now an effort could be made to raise, from within BR and through grants, the remainder of the estimated £3 million needed for full restoration of Ribblehead.

Design work began almost immediately. The General Manager authorised the engineers to prepare drawings, specifications and contract documents for a full structural restoration of the viaduct.

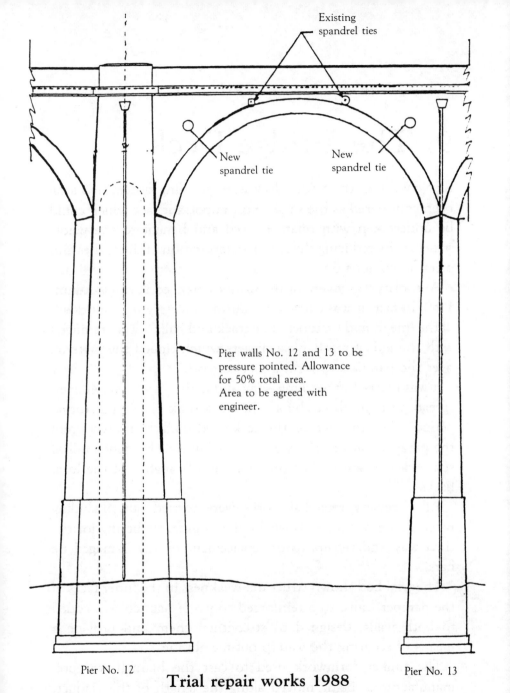

Existing
spandrel ties

New
spandrel tie

New
spandrel tie

Pier walls No. 12 and 13 to be
pressure pointed. Allowance
for 50% total area.
Area to be agreed with
engineer.

Pier No. 12

Pier No. 13

Trial repair works 1988

(N.B. new spandrel ties not used)

9: The Bridge Deck

RENEWAL of the bridge deck waterproofing system had long been considered as the single most important task which could be undertaken with relative speed and benefit to the whole structure by reducing the rate of deterioration of the arches and piers on completion.

Authority was given for the work to proceed during autumn, 1989. In fact, it was carried out during a fortnight's shut-down of the line in mid-October. The track and ballast were removed with the aid of mechanical diggers which tipped the material over the parapets to form a service road.

It was three-shift working—day and night—with over 40 men spread over the three shifts. The work took place in a stormy period, when the men on the deck needed all the protection of the parapet walls as the viaduct was buffeted by winds full of spite. Heavy rain soaked the moor and brought out the local becks.

All necessary remedial works were carried out, including patch filling of the voids left by the original timbering for the travelway and repairs to or replacement of any damaged tie bars.

The trial had shown structural weakness in the inner faces of the parapet walls, so a reinforced concrete haunch was added to both walls, designed to strengthen them and provide a means of securing the waterproof membrane.

The timber formwork used to cast the haunch was pre-manufactured, being moved along the length of the viaduct, three at a time, working from the south end, each night, the following day being spent on casting the haunch.

The displaced ballast on the service road supported the vehicles bringing ready-mixed concrete for the making of the haunches. Concrete was pumped from the valley bottom to bridge deck level by a special pump with a boom 140 ft long.

When the casting of the haunch was complete and the concrete had cured, the entire viaduct deck was overlaid with a tough, durable, rubberised membrane cushioned on both top and bottom to prevent accidental puncturing by the replacement ballast or any other foreign body.

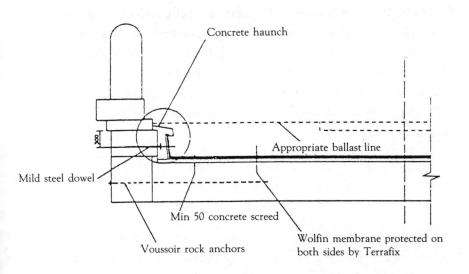

Cross section of deck

(After waterproofing)

A mobile crane fitted with a 140 ft jib was used to lift rolls of the membrane (Wolfin 1B) from ground level to the deck at an elevation of over 100 ft.

The membrane was finally secured to the sides of the concrete haunches on each side of the bridge deck before the entire deck was reballasted. A total of 2,500 tonnes of new ballast were transported to the site from North Wales and to it was added the 500 tonnes of old ballast which had been found suitable for re-use.

Following re-ballasting, the track—which had been removed some two weeks earlier and stockpiled between the south end of the viaduct and Ribblehead station—was re-laid.

On the Sunday, wind, mist and heavy rain combined into atrocious conditions. Yet the viaduct was handed back to traffic at 06.30 hrs on Monday, October 30, only half an hour later than planned, after a significant achievement carried out in grim weather. Incidentally, no scheduled trains were delayed by the delay in handing back viaduct to traffic.

The waterproofing works were carried out at a cost of £400,000, which included the provision of the concrete haunch.

Scaffolding on the East Face of Ribblehead, October 1990.
At the peak of the works, the maximum accumulated
length of scaffold tubing in use was 150,000 feet.

Above—Block replacement at the corner of a pier.
From top to bottom—Original block of limestone badly cracked towards the right; a gap where a badly eroded block had been removed and screwed props inserted to maintain support to the upper masonry prior to infilling with concrete; and a replacement block of concrete, cast within a fibreglass facial mould, using a black dye to match the natural colour of the stone.

Opposite—Liza Pugh, a B R quantity surveyor, inspecting a block on a voussoir prior to carrying out precise measurements.

Above—A B R bricklayer preparing to carry out repairs under an arch to a cracked area between the tails of the voussoirs and the arch brickwork.

Opposite—Pointing a pier at Ribblehead. It was originally intended to point selected areas but eventually the whole structure had the old mortar chipped out and new mortar provided using a pressure pointing system.

Three personalities during the restoration. *Top left:* Tony Freschini, resident engineer. *Bottom left:* Geoff Bounds, project manager. *Right:* Meloni Denley, resident engineer.

Motive power at Ribblehead. *Above:* West Country "Tor Valley" (34027) photographed (with B R permission) from the scaffolding. *Centre:* Class 45 with a Glasgow-Nottingham express, early 1970s. *Below:* A Class 156 Super Sprinter.

Ribblehead after restoration. For the first time for many years we can picture the famous structure as it was on completion in the 1870s. (This view from the north-west, includes Penyghent).

10: On to Completion

ATTENTION now turned to restoring the remainder of the viaduct, taking into account the report of the resident engineer, which noted the types of defect that would probably be found. The report had concluded that all the piers should be strengthened by the injection of grout and that steel bars would be needed to stitch and tie together the masonry blocks within the piers.

Defective brickwork within the arches was to be replaced. Stainless steel rock anchors were prescribed to tie the masonry voussoirs to the arch brickwork. Unrepairable masonry blocks were to be replaced and all loose masonry removed and repaired as necessary. When the main repairs were completed, all the masonry joints were to be re-pointed.

Whatever happened, the integrity of Ribblehead viaduct as a large Victorian structure in a most conspicuous position would be maintained. It was recognised that the metal plates installed during previous repairs to the piers and spandrel areas—items which were most definitely post-Victorian—would have to remain. Nor was it economically possible to restore the colour balance of brickwork under the arches where red brick had been used in areas of blue brick.

The unsightly rail-strapping and girdling on Piers No. 7 to No. 9 were removed. So was the concrete strengthening to the corners of Pier No. 11.

At Ribblehead, the workforce became masters of "invisible mending". The plans envisaged that the steel bars (rock anchors) to be installed would be set within the structure and unplated. (In the event, about 1,200 such bars were fitted). Neither would there be any outward trace of the holes drilled for grouting, for such drilling would be through the horizontal bed joints, which would be re-pointed. (Nearly 5,000 holes were drilled in the piers).

The contract for the main body of the repair work was placed with Morrison Shand in June 1990. The commencement of work at the site, in July 1990, was marked by a staged contract signing ceremony. The value of the contract placed on Morrison Shand (£1,833,000) covered all repair works to the piers, spandrels and parapet walls (external).

The repair work to the brick arches, which was regarded as specialist in nature—for repairs had to take place without closing the line—was awarded to British Rail's Construction Manager, who had submitted an estimate for £188,000.

Included in the overall cost of the works was a sum of £164,000, representing supervision by British Rail's Civil Engineering department.

The total estimated cost of the main repair works was therefore £2,185,000. When the cost of the trial repair and waterproofing works were added to this sum, it totalled £2,965,000, a figure remarkably close to the estimated cost of £3,000,000, as calculated following the trial repairs.

The main repair works, which began in July 1990, had an anticipated completion date of November 1991. This timescale allowed for a winter shut-down from November 1990 to early April 1991. In the event, winter working was possible until December.

At its peak, the labour force consisted of 50 men of various skills, about half the number of masons and joiners associated with the viaduct during the construction period.

Wind and Weather

To the workers at Ribblehead viaduct, the worst elements of the weather were frost and wind. Much of the repair work involved the use of materials which needed to be mixed with cement and water before use. Consequently, they were sensitive to sub-zero temperatures, which regularly occur at Ribblehead in winter, persisting for several days.

At wind speeds above 50 mph, a worker would require to use one hand in simply holding on to the scaffold. Above this speed, the access platform boarding might be dislodged. So all work was stopped when the wind speed, either continuously or in gusts, exceeded that figure.

Although all the boarding had to be securely fastened down, boards at the upper mast levels of the platform were often disturbed during lengthy storms. The main scaffolding withstood the most severe weather without being damaged.

Works of this type and magnitude demanded working platforms which permitted access to every part of the structure. Thus did scaffolding become one of the most expensive items of the works, accounting for over £0.4m of the contract price.

Grouting the Piers

Prior to grouting, holes 1 metre deep were drilled through the masonry joints into the core of the piers. Well over 200 holes were driven into each pier, the holes being positioned in a regular pattern, as devised by the engineers, to suit the individual condition of each pier.

With the completion of the drilling, a mixture of one part of cement and one part of fly-ash was pumped through the holes into the piers, working from bottom to top, level by level. As with all such work,the amount of grout taken by each hole varied and thus the amount taken per intermediate pier varied from 9 tonnes to nearly 50 tonnes. Additionally, the grouting of the voids to the King Piers consumed almost 300 tonnes of grout per pier.

Replacing Cracked Stones

Only two defective corner stones were replaced during the trial works, which was thought not to represent the state of the piers generally. Provision was made for the replacement of an average of four in five blocks on each pier. In practice, the number requiring this treatment more than trebled.

Piers numbered 7-9 and also No.11 were found to be in a poor state. Pier No.7 alone had no less than 40 defective blocks. The replacement process had to be carried out slowly and carefully, support being maintained to the adjacent masonry at all times.

The initial stage consisted of the removal of sufficient of each failed block to permit special adjustable props to be inserted to support the blocks above. When this had been done, the remainder of the defective blocks could be taken away.

The replacement of a hand-dressed limestone block by traditional dressed stone was neither practical or economical. A stone was removed and the strain taken by special adjustable props which were sacrificial in nature, being left as concrete was poured into a fibre-glass shutter to fill the gap.

In order not to mar the appearance of the historic structure, BR arranged for its own workshop to manufacture a range of fibreglass moulds of various sizes, these being shaped to match the profile of the existing masonry.

Prior to concreting, the moulds were fixed in position securely to the face of the pier using timber battens, metal bolts and props. The void behind was filled with concrete. After the new concrete had cured for 24 hours, the moulds were removed and

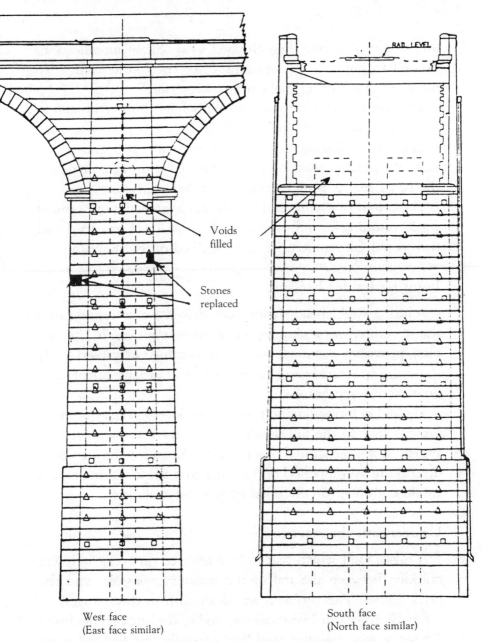

Voids
filled

Stones
replaced

West face
(East face similar)

South face
(North face similar)

Typical repairs of king piers 6, 12 and 18

Key: △ = Grout holes ☐ = Stitching bar holes

any surplus concrete then chipped away. Slight modifications needed to improve the appearance of the blocks were then made using a cutting tool on a power drill.

The concrete blocks would normally have dried to an almost white appearance unsuited to their situation in a Victorian viaduct. Experiments were carried out with dyes and a particularly dark one was chosen to be mixed with the concrete in the belief that it would weather to a limestony hue.

The colour of the natural blocks was lightened by a "cement wash" resulting from the repair works, and it was reckoned that this would take some time to be washed off by the rain.

Pointing Under Pressure

Pointing Ribblehead, to prevent driven water seeping into the structure, was a vital aspect of the restoration. In the first plan, provision was made for patch-pointing but subsequently the entire structure was re-pointed to avoid variable quality and unattractive appearance.

The old pointing having been painstakingly raked out, mortar was shot to the full depth of every crack using a pressure system. It was recognised that even this superior pointing would deteriorate over a period of time and that the limestone blocks would continue to be eroded by gradual spalling.

Underneath the Arches

A major fault which had to be addressed on every arch was cracking between the tail of the masonry voussoirs and the brick arches. This problem was dealt with in three stages.

Firstly, every third voussoir was tied to the brick arches using 2.5 metre long stainless steel bars carefully installed following diamond core drilling through the faces of the stones.

Ribblehead rests on bedrock, though a story that it was built "on wool" is still circulating. Could it be that fleeces were placed at the edges of the shafts to stop a seepage of water? Or was the mention of wool a reference to money from the Bradford Woolmen helping to finance the undertaking, the ultimate cost of which was far in excess of the estimate? As for the Ribblehead piers, trial borings were made during the first winter of the construction period (1869-70). Shafts were sunk to the solid rock, up to 25 feet down through peat and clay. The base of a pier was set on concrete laid upon the rock. When, not many years later, a railway was constructed between Fort William and Mallaig, in north-west Scotland, viaducts were being made entirely of concrete.

Secondly, all loose and damaged brickwood in the vicinity of the cracks was replaced using new bricks selected to match the colour of those round about. Finally, the remaining part of the crack was sealed with a special mortar.

It was an uncommon privilege to stand on scaffolding at an elevation of almost 100 ft and watch two brickies at work in a way little changed in over a century. A hole was drilled to admit a T-shaped implement, one of several devised to hold an arch of metal equivalent to the arch of the viaduct but leaving space for the positioning of baulks of wood to hold newly-introduced brick for the two days necessary for the mortar to dry.

The repair works taught those involved much about the requirements of huge masonry structures. It was concluded by the engineers that the experience would be invaluable when dealing with the other large viaducts on the line and their repair would be even more cost effective.

All the repair work requiring scaffolding was completed by Christmas, 1991, leaving only minor works and site tidying to be completed early in 1992.

Top of parapet

L level

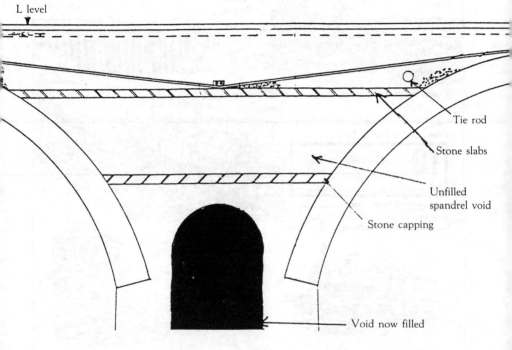

Tie rod

Stone slabs

Unfilled
spandrel void

Stone capping

Void now filled

Cross section of king piers 6, 12 and 18

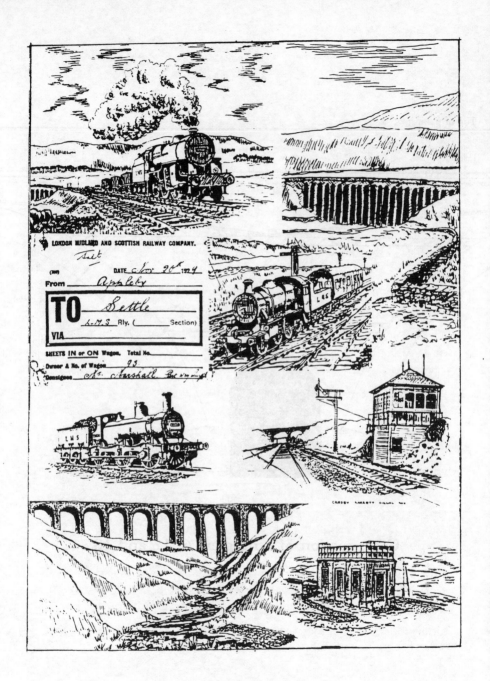

LONDON MIDLAND AND SCOTTISH RAILWAY COMPANY.

DATE Nov 26th 1924

From Appleby

TO Settle

L.M.S Rly. (Section)

VIA

SHEETS IN or ON Wagon. Total No.

Owner & No. of Wagon 93

Consignee Mr. Marshall

11: Public Relations

BRITISH RAIL, aware of public interest, and anxious that visitors should not trespass or interfere with the work in hand, took the unusual step of providing a visitor cabin, which was opened in the late summer of 1990 on the east side of the viaduct, close to the public right of way.

The staffing was provided by members of the Friends of the Settle-Carlisle. They were in attendance each week-end during October, 1990 and, encouraged, they returned to staff the cabin on some weekdays and at week-ends through the summer of 1991.

The standard of display was raised by special art work prepared by British Rail's public affairs department at York. Information panels detailed the history of the viaduct and the work in progress, with periodic updates. The sale of publications benefited the Friends who, in turn, benefit the railway by their interest and grants.

The number of visitors rose when, in 1991, the cabin had to be moved away from the foot of the viaduct to a position where it was also seen by walkers heading for Whernside and Dent. Permission to use this new site was readily given by Dr J A Farrer, of Ingleborough Estate (whose forebears had sold land to the *Midland* company on which Ribblehead viaduct stands).

The cabin—and its cheerful voluntary staff—suffered considerable buffeting from the wind and, on one occasion, it was blown round through an arc of 90 degrees. The visitor centre was finally removed from site by lorry on December 2, 1991. By then, the works were almost completed. The displays were taken into the safe-keeping of British Rail for future use.

Raising the Cash

British Rail had only one possible response to the reprieve of the Settle & Carlisle: to square itself up to the repair of Ribblehead viaduct.

In the two and a-half years between the line's reprieve and the completion of the major restoration at Ribblehead, BR used about £850,500 of its limited financial resources on this structure alone. The cost of restoration was almost exactly £3,000,000 and the huge shortfall was met by handsome grants, notably:

> English Heritage—£1,000,000
> Settle & Carlisle Railway Trust—£499,000
> Railway Heritage Trust—£300,000
> Rural Development Commission—£100,000

The English Heritage grant contribution represented the single largest grant awarded by that organisation and a significant marker as to the importance it places on the heritage of such a major structure on the Settle-Carlisle line. The viaduct had already been scheduled as an Ancient Monument.

The terms of the grant offer were on the basis of 40% of the grant eligible works, to a ceiling of £1,000,000. The original grant offer was £926,989 which equated to 40% of the main repair and waterproofing works. Additional repairs that proved necessary to piers 18-23 and to the associated arches took the grant contribution up to the ceiling of £1,000,000 in late 1991.

The grant, which represents 37% of the cost of the waterproofing and main repair works, was conditional on BR continuing to operate the line. It was also specified that if BR dispose of the viaduct within 25 years of completion of the repairs, a reducing percentage of the total grant is repayable to English Heritage from 100% in Year One to 0% in Year Twenty-five.

Payment of the grant was made on the basis of certificates submitted by BR each month and with staged grant payments being made at 40% of the value of the works done. Detailed discussions took place between BR and English Heritage with regard to the method of repairs and the materials to be used.

The grant given by The Settle & Carlisle Railway Trust was made payable over three years starting in 1990-91, the final payment to be made in 1992/3. The total contribution of £499,500 was split into annual sums of £168,000, with a third and final contribution of £163,500.

The Settle & Carlisle Railway Trust was formally established with full charitable status in March, 1990. The Trust sprang from the Friends of the Settle & Carlisle line and its aims are to assist with funding the restoration of the "built heritage" of the Leeds-Settle-Carlisle line and assisting in the interpretation of the history of the line.

Its grant, representing the pledged contributions of a number of local authorities, was passed to BR via the Trust as a convenient means of co-ordinating payment. Contributions were made by the following authorities:

North Yorkshire CC, Richmondshire DC, Carlisle CC, Cumbria CC, Lancashire CC, Eden DC, Craven DC, Skipton TC, Calderdale MBC, Settle TC, Yorkshire Dales National Park Committee, Bradford MBC and Friends of the Settle-Carlisle Line.

The Railway Heritage Trust, chaired by the Hon Sir William McAlpine, Bart., is funded by the British Railways Board. Such funding helps to cover the cost of specific architectural works which the Trust considers appropriate.

The money is allocated to listed buildings owned by British Rail. Given the level of funds which the Trust normally has at its disposal, it was a handsome gesture to make available £50,000 towards the cost of trial repairs in 1988 and £250,000 towards the main restoration.

The Trust thereby covered about 10% of the total cost of repairs to the viaduct, the contributions being conditional on the grant being expended within the appropriate financial year.

The Rural Development Commission pledged grant support to the repair of Ribblehead on condition that the grant was spent within the financial year 1989/90. In view of this proviso, the grant of £100,000 was used to offset the cost of the waterproofing work.

12: Into the Future

TEN years have elapsed since the condition of Ribblehead viaduct became a major area of concern when considering the future of the Settle-Carlisle line. Ribblehead is now in as good or a better state than when it was built.

Yet, natural processes being what they are, its condition will once again slowly deteriorate as the blocks of local limestone, exposed to wind and weather, continue to flake and crack, when yet more replacements will be needed. At least the most seriously cracked have been taken out to be substituted by concrete.

Ribblehead has an attractive appearance now that the concrete and metal "splints" have gone. It is not difficult to pick out the corner stones that were replaced but hopefully the concrete will weather well and the darkish dye used in it will, at the same time, take on the pearl-grey tone of limestone.

Before the restoration, somewhat garish signs were fixed to Ribblehead viaduct warning of the chances of falling masonry. Such an eventuality occurs naturally during the life of any large structure as it is affected by use and weathering.

As there is but one right of way under the viaduct, this point can be made in a telling but less conspicuous way in the future. A small stone cairn is to be designed. On it will be a bronze plaque commemorating the restoration of the viaduct and mentioning the organisations prominently associated with it.

A note on the plaque will direct visitors to the possibility of falling masonry, which may from time to time be no more than a flake of limestone from one of the innumerable blocks, part of the inevitable ageing process of a structure of this type.

One of the last jobs when the current programme of repairs ended was to level the ground beneath the arches to provide a sound base from which to undertake future inspection or maintenance work.

The completion of the repairs at Ribblehead does not mark the end of the challenge to maintain the Settle-Carlisle heritage. This railway, which goes mountaineering, continues to offer an all-weather, finely-engineered route.

The Settle-Carlisle is the only railway line in Britain which has been designated for its entire length as a conservation area. With a host of other major structures between Settle and Carlisle, the effort now switches into bringing up to scratch Ribblehead's sister viaducts and the host of small bridges, all of which are vital in maintaining continuity of traffic on our best-known line.

They must be maintained as part of an on-going operation. It will be a costly operation calling, as with Ribblehead, for BR's limited finances to be augmented by grants from those who wish to ensure that the Settle-Carlisle really does have a future.

Appendices

1. PRINCIPAL WORKERS WHO AT SOME TIME WERE CONNECTED WITH THE PROJECT:

British Rail:

Project Resident Engineer: A.P. Freschini.

Appointed by J C Elliott, Regional Civil Engineer for London Midland Region. Initially, this appointment was for the 1988 Trial Repair contract, thence for the 1989 Contract for Waterproofing the bridge deck and subsequently for the 1990-2 Main Repair Work contract.

Tony's duties have required him to represent and act directly on behalf of the Regional Civil Engineer administering the contract and to supervise the works, ensuring they are completed satisfactorily and safely to programme.

At Ribblehead, Tony also specified the types and extent of the individual repairs and agreed through discussion with the contractor on measures to ensure the safety of the operatives and maintenance of the structural stability of the viaduct at all times.

Project Manager for the Settle-Carlisle Line: Geoff Bounds.

The appointment, by Regional Railways North East, was made in 1989, and applies to projects throughout the 72-mile long length of the railway.

At Ribblehead, Geoff represented the General Manager with specific responsibility for ensuring the completion of the works on time and to budget.

Additionally, he co-ordinated, with full regard to safety, the works of the various railway departments involved.

Geoff liaised with the external sponsors and obtained financial backing for the Ribblehead project from internal and external sources.

Other members of BR staff involved were: Resident Engineers, Mrs M Denley, Mr D Steer, Mr G Martin, Mr M De Voil. Clerks of Works: Mr F R Clare, Mr. I Ibberson, Mr J Charlton. Quantity Surveyor: Ms L Pugh. Project Design Engineer, Mr M V Sumpter. Secretary, Ms S Winstanley. Mr B Durango made the fibre glass shuttering.

BR Construction Group North:

Messrs T Clark, J Smith, T Edgar, T Cordley, R Banks, D Clark, D Adams, R Pickering, A Dutton, B Gleave, P Davis; Mr J Mason, R Arling, Quantity Surveyor, R Parkes.

Morrison Shand:

Mr I J Jones, Site Agent; Mr R A Barker, Contracts Manager; Mr D Thackray, Site Engineer; Mr M Camm, Managing Quantity Surveyor; Mr P Greene, Works Manager; Mr A Ford, Mr D Jones, Quantity Surveyors; Mr K. Swanson, General Operative.

Speedy Scaffolders:

Mr B Eades, Mr T Rawlings, Contracts Managers; Mr Steve Hall, Foreman Scaffolder. Messrs G Unsworth, S Hall, J Robson, A Maddon, I Fazakerley, M Tate, D Wheeler, P Menary, A Wells, P Rigby.

Keller Colcrete:

Mr R D Holmes, Contract Engineer; Mr J Stanley, General Foreman; Mr J Hall, snr and Mr J Aitken, foremen, Mr D Stanley, Charge Hand.

Also: Messrs J Watson, W Mackie, C Watson, A Greenfield, R Chiltern, S Marriot, P Hinchcliffe, D Dinsdale, P Brash, G Sharpe, W McCormack, P Patton, snr, N Patton, J Leighton, M Westwick, I O'Brien, G Patrick, P Hibbert, J Hall, jnr, H Breeze, O Pigott, M Guinan, T Rose.

W Brodie, D Halifax, S Moffit, J Smith, J Davies, T Miller, D Lycett, P Patton, jnr, M Moore, A Fenton, G Swanson, K Kinsey, N Lindsey, E Boote, R Murray, T Lyons, A Wordsworth, P Heenan, A Smiley, A Kit, D Hide, M Webb, G Noble, C Shaw, M Trafford, K Stubbs, G Farquharson, P Pugh, R Morris, N Pennington, G McCrea, P Griffiths.

C Boyle, J. Walker, G Fearnley, D Thompson, A Turner, M Thornton, A Fulford, P Reed, D Holloway, N Compton, K Grant, G Reynolds, A Wood, K. Cuthbertson, I Freeman, M Wordsworth.

2. SUMMARY OF PRINCIPAL WORKS UNDERTAKEN WHEN WATERPROOFING THE BRIDGE DECK, AUTUMN, 1989:

Ballast and fill cleared from deck area—3,000 tonnes
Re-used ballast—500 tonnes
Imported new railway ballast—2,500 tonnes
Concrete for bridge deck and new parapet haunch—220 cub.metres
Steel reinforcement—5 tonnes
Area of deck covered with Wolfin IB waterproof membrane—2,647 squ.metres

Area of material used to protect Wolfin membrane—5,294 squ.metres
Single line long welded track removed and replaced—450 metres

3. QUANTITIES USED, PROVISIONAL REPAIR, DURING THE MAIN CONTRACT, 1990-1992

Drilling and Grouting Works
Number of 37mm diameter holes drilled percussively—4,686
Accumulated length of 37mm holes—6,760 metres
Tonnage of grout injected (PFA/Cement)—1,420 tonnes
Rock Anchor Works
Number of 37mm diameter holes drilled using diamond coring drills—1,295
Accumulated length of holes drilled for rock anchors—3,471 metres
Number of stainless steel rock anchors installed (various lengths from 1 metre to 2.5 metres)—1,200
Renewal of downpipes and fittings—986 metres
Masonry repair (repointing works)—15,500 squ.metres
Defective masonry block (replacement works) in piers—289
Defective voussoirs replaced—35
Scaffolding—In general, between 4 to 6 piers were scaffolded at any one time, dismantling and erection proceeding from south to north along the viaduct. At the peak of the works, the maximum accumulated length of scaffold tubing in use was 150,000 ft.

4. GLOSSARY OF ENGINEERING TERMS
Compiled by Tony Freschini

Core Drill. Equipment for drilling holes which works by rotary action. Core drills are often used to extract continuous cores of rock for inspection.

Grout. Carefully proportioned liquid mixture of cement P F A and water designed to be pumped into the structure via the grout holes. After injection, the grout sets to form a solid material of great strength.

Grout Hole. Hole drilled to facilitate the passage of grout.

Percussive Drill. Equipment for drilling holes. It works by rotary and hammer action.

Pressure Pointing. Process of undertaking pointing works using mechanical equipment powered by compressed air. Using this method, it is possible to fully fill deep open joints.

Pulverised Fly Ash (P F A). Fine powdery ash which arises from combustion in the boilers of coal-fired power stations and is used in the building industry as a lightweight bulk filling material. When blended with cement and water, the resultant mixture, on setting, has considerable strength.

Rock Anchors. Steel bars of varying lengths used to tie or strengthen defective areas of brickwork or masonry. The bars are set in high strength grout.

Stitching Bars. Steel bars of varying lengths used in groups positioned in a criss-cross pattern to tie or strengthen particular areas of masonry. (Such bars are installed in a similar way to rock anchors).

Void, intermediate pier. Small voids or empty areas are often to be found in the filled core of this type of pier, where the fill material has been lost because of weathering or where it had been inadequately packed during construction.

Void, king pier. An unfilled space within a pier running from foundation level to the lower spandrel level, being part of the original design. Such a void has been filled with grout during the restoration at Ribblehead.

Void, spandrel. Unfilled space between the spandrel walls and bridge deck, being part of the original design.

A Postscript

THE LINE is a tribute to Victorian engineering skills and is now undeniably part of our National Heritage. This can only remain the case if it is retained as a working railway... The line meets important social needs and is coming into its own as an important tourist and recreational attraction.

Commissioning authorities, following publication of the PEIDA report in the summer of 1984

VOUSSOIR :-
VOODSWAAR